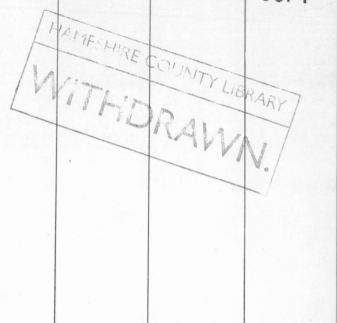

BRAHMS

Songs of Love

(LIEBESLIEDER)

opus 52

waltzes for piano duet with optional voices.
Arrangement for SSA
by REGINALD JOHNSON

English words
by W. G. Rothery

NOVELLO
Borough Green Sevenoaks Kent

Performances of this arrangement should be given with the original piano duet accompaniment, which is available on hire. The piano solo version is for rehearsal purposes only.

SONGS OF LOVE
(*LIEBESLIEDER*)
English words by W. G. ROTHERY
MUSIC BY
JOHANNES BRAHMS
Opus 52
Arranged for S.S.A. by REGINALD JOHNSON

1

In slow waltz time

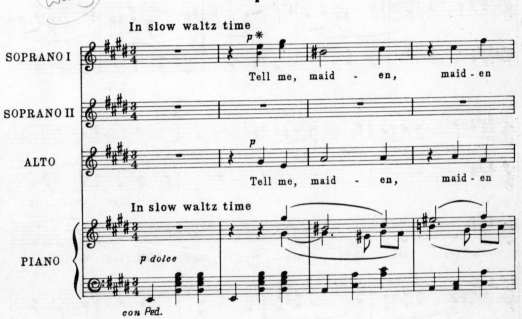

Tell me, maid - en, maid - en

dear - est, In dis - dain — thy — lov - er spurn - ing,

*Alternative notes in small type

18286

MADE IN ENGLAND

Will thy heart be cold for ev - er?

treat thee, Will thy heart be cold for ev - er?

treat thee,

Nay, O tell_____ me,_ tell_____ me I_____ may meet thee.

Nay, O tell_____ me,_ tell_____ me, tell me, Nay, I

Nay, I

p dolce

care_____ not so_____ to lan - guish, All_____ the world's de -

care_____ not so_____ to lan - guish, All_____ the world's de -

Tearing on!

12

Juliet & Christine

3

SOPRANO I
O ye maid - ens! you en - chain me,

SOPRANO II
O ye maid - ens! you en - chain me,

PIANO

Though so oft - en you dis - dain me,

Though so oft - en you dis - dain me,

Ped. ✱ Ped. ✱

But for you I'd be a fri - ar,

But for you I'd be a fri - ar,

8

18286

creepy.

5

SOPRANO I
The young vine's twin - ing tend -
say, ye droop - ing tend -

SOPRANO II

ALTO
The young vine's twin - ing tend -
say, ye droop - ing tend -

PIANO
p dolce
legato

10 12

rils to mo - ther earth are droop - ing low.
rils, why may you not to heav'n a - rise?

I see a ten - der
O tell me ten - der

rils to mo - ther earth are droop - ing low. I see a ten - der
rils, why may you not to heav'n a - rise? O tell me ten - der

10 12

11   **13**

O   How

maid - en, whose tears in si - lence flow;   How
maid - en, why tears be - dew your eyes?

maid - en, whose tears in si - lence flow;
maid - en, why tears be - dew your eyes?   O

11   **13**

12

6

14

16

18286

7

8

9

26

28

10

18286

* Small notes are optional

34

18286

13

SOPRANO I

Solo

O'er the sea___ the swal - lows fly, the swal -

SOPRANO II

O'er the sea___ the swal - lows fly, the swal -

PIANO

48

- lows fly, Home - ward nev - er

- lows fly, Home - ward nev - er

tir - ing, So the

tir - ing, So the

36

heart for rest doth sigh, Love and

heart for rest doth sigh, Love and

peace de - sir - ing, sir - ing.

peace de - sir - ing, sir - ing.

14

SOPRANO I

1 See how clear the moon - beams
2 Weave a - round her heart a

ALTO

1 See how clear the moon - beams
2 Weave a - round her heart a

PIANO

p dolce

15

When the stars are peep - ing;

When the stars are peep - ing;

When the stars are peep - ing;

Dear - est heart, one kiss I

Dear - est heart, one kiss I

Dear - est heart, one kiss I

crave, While the world is

crave, While the world is

crave, While the world is

16

Animato
SOPRANO I
O, love is a deep dark well,
SOPRANO II
O, love is a deep dark well,
ALTO
O, love is a
Where - in it is
Animato
PIANO
53
sirs, Where - in it is fool - ish to dwell, sirs;
sirs, Where - in it is fool - ish to dwell, sirs;
deep dark well, sirs, a well, sirs,
fool - ish to dwell, sirs;
53
I tum-bled there - in, un -
I tum - bled there - in, un - heed - ing, I
I tum-bled there - in, un -

griev - - ous plight.

griev - - ous plight.

griev - - ous plight.

sfz

f

Sheenagh   Solo   **17**

Espressivo   *p*

SOPRANO I

O stray not, dear heart,

PIANO

p dolce

con Ped.

56

midst yon - der fair mea - dow way, The flow'rs a -

bout thy feet will harm thee, So wet

p

18

48

ve - ry soul is sha - ken With

ve - ry soul is sha - ken With

ve - ry soul is sha - ken With

love and love's sweet sor - row, with

love and love's sweet sor - row, with

love and love's sweet sor - row, with

love and love's sweet sor - row, And

love and love's sweet sor - row, And

love and love's sweet sor - row, And

Cantatas & Choral Suites

FOR FEMALE OR BOYS' VOICES

Brahms	SONGS OF LOVE (Liebeslieder) *waltzes arr for SSA & piano by Reginald Johnson*
George Dyson	A CHRISTMAS GARLAND *cantata for M-S solo, SSA & piano*
	LET'S GO A-MAYING *cantata for SSA & piano**
Colin Hand	STABAT MATER *cantata for SSA & orchestra or piano**
	WOLCUM YOLE *carol sequence for SA & piano*
Handel	MUSIC FROM 'SEMELE' *arr for SSA & piano (opt T solo) by Maurice Blower*
Tony Hewitt-Jones	EPIGRAMS *for unaccompanied SSA*
Trevor Hold	THREE SONGS OF THE COUNTRYSIDE *for two equal voices & piano*
Michael Hurd	CANTICLES OF THE VIRGIN MARY *four 15th century English carols for SSA & piano*
	MISSA BREVIS *for SSA & organ or piano**
Wilfrid Mellers	PRIMAVERA *six canzonets for unaccompanied SSA*
Bernard Naylor	KUBLA KHAN *cantata for SSAA & piano*
	STABAT MATER *for double choir & orchestra**
Pergolesi	STABAT MATER *cantata for SA soli, SA & piano**
John C. Phillips	CHANTONS NOEL *three French carols arr for SSA & piano**
	WORLD REJOICE! *suite of traditional carols from five nations* *arr SA, SSA, piano, strings & percussion**
Purcell	COME YE SONS OF ART *arr for SSA & piano by Maurice Blower**
Christopher Steel	GETHSEMANE *cantata for SA & piano**
	MARY MAGDALENE *cantata for SSA & piano**

*orchestral material available on hire

---

inspection copies available on request